Jack Teaches His Friends to Be KIDSAFE!

Sally Berenzweig, MEd, MA
& Cherie Benjoseph, LCSW

Illustrated by Lilah Cohen

KidSafe®
FOUNDATION
working together to keep kids safe

The information provided in this book is designed to provide helpful information on the subjects discussed. This book is not intended to replace the advice of or treatment by psychologists or other health care professionals.

KidSafe Foundation, Inc.
info@KidSafeFoundation.org
www.KidSafeFoundation.org

ISBN: 978-0-9989529-3-2

Printed in the United States
by Minuteman Press of Boca Raton, Florida.

Second Edition • Fourth printing

Thank you to all the adults who understand
the importance of teaching children prevention
education, support our programs, and
read our books to their children.

Thank you to all the children who
have enjoyed our books and have
learned important safety skills.
May you all stay KidSafe!

Working together to keep KidSafe,

Cherie and Sally

Cofounders of KidSafe Foundation

Foreword

KidSafe Foundation holds a special place in my heart. As a survivor of sexual abuse, I appreciate how KidSafe places an emphasis on giving children a voice and teaching them how to follow their instincts, even if it is a person they love and trust who is harming them. This book will help parents have an open dialogue with their children about all the safety issues children can face, including peer pressure, bullying, internet dangers, and abuse. *Jack teaches his friends to be KidSafe!* is unique as it also offers a section for adults to further understand and encourage use of KidSafe's Language of Safety.

I encourage everyone who has children in their lives whom they love to read this book. We can protect children from harm—the key is integrating the KidSafe tools and skills into everyday parenting to best keep children safe.

—Anya Alvarez

Anya Alvarez is a golf professional, sexual abuse survivor, and KidSafe Foundation Spokesperson and Advisory Board Member. She is a contributing writer to *twoday* magazine on issues of teen dating violence, a speaker for the Liz Claiborne Organization's "Love Is Not Abuse," and was nominated by *Seventeen* magazine as one of the most influential teens in America. Anya has appeared on *CBS Early Morning News* and on *Dr. Phil.* She is a member of LPGA's Symetra Tour and is featured on the Golf Channel show *The Big Break Atlantis.*

Introduction to KidSafe

KidSafe Foundation is a 501(c)3 nonprofit dedicated to providing prevention education to children and adults with the goal of decreasing child abuse, bullying, and internet dangers. With the purchase of this book you are helping to support KidSafe Foundation. 100% of the monies received from this book will go directly to the Foundation to continue to bring prevention education programs and materials to children and adults.

Why We Wrote This Book

It is our belief that children learn from other children and writing *Jack Teaches His Friends to Be KidSafe!* gives children the opportunity to learn through Jack, who wants his friends to be safe. To that end, he teaches them nine important safety skills he learned from his parents. "Jack" educates his friends through rhyme and beautiful illustrations, helping children learn life skills in a fun and memorable way.

Jack Teaches His Friends to Be KidSafe! offers adults, including parents and professionals, a comfortable, child friendly, developmentally appropriate way to converse with their children about personal safety. We encourage all adults to integrate nine safety skills into their natural daily parenting by using the KidSafe Language of Safety. (See Glossary)

For more information about the KidSafe SAFE AND SMART BOOK SERIES including the 2011 Children's Literary Classic award-winning book, *My Body Is Special and Belongs to Me!*, visit www.kidsafefoundation.org.

My parents taught me to be KidSafe.
They taught me many safety rules.
And now I want to share KidSafe
with all my friends at school!

Rule number one is **always stay close to your trusted adult**, the adult who is with you the most.
Your trusted adult can be your mom, dad, and aunt or uncle too.
Just think of all the people who take good care of you.

When you are walking across the street or going out to play, close to your grown-up is the safest place to stay.

3

Staying near your grown-up is meant to keep you safe.
Stay close in public restrooms . . . and in *every* other place!

The second rule I want my friends to know about is *always* **Check First** with a grown-up before
   you go out.
Also ask your grown-up in charge before you
   answer the door.
Keeping us KidSafe is what this rule is for.

Before you go out to play
or get in someone's car,
You need to Check First with
your grown-up,
so they know where you are.

The third rule is very important to know.
It's the **Five-Step Back** rule, and here's how it goes:
When you are walking to school or playing outside, take five steps back if a car repeatedly drives by.

If the driver stops to talk to you,
Yell "No!" Run and Tell is what you need to do.

Adults you don't know should not ask
kids for help or try to talk to you.
If they try, Yell "No!" Run and Tell
is the skill that you could use.

The fourth rule I want you to know is the
   Safe and Unsafe Touch rule, and here's how it goes:
A safe touch is a touch that makes you feel comfortable,
   safe, and loved,
such as a pat on your back, or a gentle hug.

An unsafe touch can make you uncomfortable and sad.
You might be confused and frightened, and you may feel mad.
If you get a touch that's confusing to you,
telling a trusted adult is the right thing to do.

"It is never your fault!"
Is what a trusted adult should say.
Never Keep Secrets,
can help you stay safe every day!

The rule about secrets is they are not always your friend.
A secret that makes you feel confused and scared needs to end.
Remember, those kind of secrets you never have to hold.
Always know it's up to YOU if you want a secret told.

Tell the secret to an
    adult you trust.
They can help in ways
    you may not see.
Adults you trust will
    keep you safe . . .
as you deserve to be!

It's a kid's right to feel safe and strong.
If someone makes you feel unsafe or worried, that person is doing something wrong!

You need to **Report** to a trusted adult, and share what is bothering you.
Because when it comes to being safe, a trusted adult will know what to do.

Don't worry that you are a tattletale, because that will never be the case!
It is always called **Reporting**.
This rule helps keep you safe.

Great job reporting!

14

You can also help yourself stay safe
by listening to the voice inside your mind.
This voice is called your conscience,
and you hear it all the time.

It helps you think things through when
you need to make the safest choice.
In KidSafe we call this rule using your
Safety Voice.

Don't forget to use your Safety Voice.
Always remember it's there!
When a friend makes an unsafe choice,
it is not a choice you have to share.

"Let's do something else" is one thing you can say.
Just because your friend makes an unsafe choice,
you don't have to do it his way.

The next rule is the **Circle of Safe Adults**,
   and this rule is a must.
When you have a problem, go straight to
   an adult you trust.
It could be your mom, dad, aunt, or teacher too.
Inside your Circle of Safe Adults are grownups
   who have proven to be there for you.

My parents taught me to be smart,
and I know that you're smart too.
If you're not sure if something is safe,
be sure to think it through.

When you follow KidSafe rules and use your Safety Voice,
it will help you make the safest and smartest choice!

My Circle of Safe Adults

19

KidSafe Foundation Glossary
Language of Safety

BAD/UNSAFE SECRET

A secret is *bad* or *unsafe* if:

- A person asks you to keep a secret and NEVER wants you to tell it;
- there is no time limit for keeping the secret;
- it makes you feel confused, scared, and/or uncomfortable. (*See* GOOD SECRET.)

BUDDY SYSTEM

The *Buddy System* means sticking close to an adult you trust when you are out. Some important places are:

- Public Restroom
- Walking to school
- Playground
- Shopping
- Traveling
- Park

CHECK FIRST

Communication between children and adults. Children should always *Check First* with the grown-up in charge before:

- Answering the door
- Helping someone older
- Taking a ride in a car
- Going outside
- Computer use
- When changing plans

CIRCLE OF SAFE ADULTS

The *Circle of Safe Adults* are the trusted adults a child has in their life they would go to if they had any problems (*see* page 17). Please do this activity with your child(ren) on an annual basis:

- Ask your child to think of three trusted adults they could go to if they had something on their mind or if they have a problem.
- Make sure you are happy with their choices.
  - You may find they chose "Coach Joe" and wonder why. You may find out important information you did not have before.
- If you do not approve of a choice or question a choice, calmly ask your child why they chose that person. Gently suggest a person you feel would be a more appropriate choice for their **Circle of Safe Adults**.

FIVE STEP BACK RULE

When a child is outside and a car (or a person) repeatedly comes by, they should automatically take *Five Steps Back*. This teaches children to be aware of their environment and personal space.

GOOD SECRET

A *Good Secret* has a happy ending and a time limit, and makes you feel happy, excited, and proud. It's a secret that the person wants you to be excited about telling, such as a surprise party or a gift.

GROWN-UP/TRUSTED ADULT

A *Grownup* or *Trusted Adult* is the adult (or adults) in a child's life who takes care of them most of the time (parent, teacher, day care provider, and so on). However, 90% of the time, a child is harmed by someone they know and trust. So it is important for parents and caregivers to educate themselves about the dangers that exist in today's world and understand that THEY have the primary responsibility of protecting their child(ren).

It is imperative to teach children to use KidSafe rules, especially Check First, which opens the lines of communication between parent and child. If your child is checking first with you before making choices, your awareness will be raised. You will have the opportunity to protect your child by guiding them to make the safest and smartest choices. (*See* CIRCLE OF SAFE ADULTS.)

REPORTING

Talking to a trusted adult about what is happening when your safety or the safety of a friend is at risk is called *Reporting*. Inform a trusted adult when it comes to the safety of yourself or your friends.

SAFE TOUCH

A *Safe Touch* is a touch a child receives or gives that makes him or her feel happy, warm, cozy, comfortable, and safe. We suggest that parents *not* use the term "good touch" as sometimes sexual abuse can "feel good" to a child, and this can cause confusion. (*See* UNSAFE TOUCH.)

SAFETY VOICE

When you are not sure what the safest and smartest choice is, use your *Safety Voice* to help guide you and think about the best choice you can make. You can say:

- "Stop, that's not safe!"
- "Let's do something else."
- "No, I don't want to. Let's do something else."

TATTLING

Telling an adult something someone did just to get them in trouble is called *Tattling*. Tattling has nothing to do with safety. (*See* REPORTING.)

UNSAFE TOUCH

An *Unsafe Touch*, received by a child, makes him or her feel uncomfortable, confused, embarrassed, awkward, nervous, worried, scared, sad, hurt, angry, and/or unsafe. These types of touches need to be reported to a trusted adult. (*See* CIRCLE OF SAFE ADULTS.)

YELL "NO!" RUN AND TELL

Children have the RIGHT to NOT listen to an adult they do not know. An adult they don't know should not be making any specific requests or demands. If an adult they don't know continues to talk to them, give your child the RIGHT to *YELL "NO!" RUN and Tell* a trusted adult. Just because it's an adult does NOT mean blind obedience! Here are some examples of common lures:

- Please help me find my lost puppy.
- Your mom is hurt; come with me.
- I need directions.
- Would you like some ice cream/candy?

Important Information for Adults

- Talking to your children about personal safety is an ongoing process, and should be a part of everyday parenting. Using this book will help you open the lines of communication and give your family a *Language of Safety*.

- When your child comes to report anything to you (small or large issues), try not to overreact. We suggest using a "poker face" when talking with your child(ren) as this helps keep the lines of communication open.

- Model good decision making. Children do what we *do*, not what we *say*.

- When a child uses their *Safety Voice* and *Reports* a safety situation to you, tell them, "great job reporting!" You want them to continue to share unsafe situations with you.

- Talk to your children about their bodies using the correct terms for their private parts.

- Never force your child to hug, kiss, or touch anyone if they do not want to. When we push children to hug, kiss, or touch an adult when they don't want to we send the message that the wants and needs of adults are more important than their own.

- Empower your children with the knowledge that *"Their bodies are special and belong to them."* This is a gift you can give your child that will last a lifetime.

If you suspect abuse or have questions regarding child abuse, please call the National ChildHelp Hotline at 1-800-4-A-CHILD (422-4453) or visit www.childhelp.org/hotline

For a list of resources visit: www.kidsafefoundation.org

"Although we need to make our children more aware of their own safety, the primary responsibility for protecting children rests with parents and other adults."

"When it comes to protecting your child from abuse, inform yourself about the stages of grooming and trust your knowledge and intuition. If you have any concerns about the adults in your child's life, investigate further and, if necessary, put a stop to any questionable relationships. Anyone who truly cares about children will understand your desire to protect your child from harm and respect your decision."

—Ken Lanning

Ken Lanning is an expert on the issue of victimization of children. He is a former Federal Bureau of Investigation (30 years) Special Agent–Behavioral Science Unit and National Center for the Analysis of Violent Crime (NCAVC). He is a founding member of the Board of Directors of the American Professional Society on the Abuse of Children (APSAC).

About the Authors

KidSafe co-founders Sally Berenzweig (top) and Cherie Benjoseph.

Sally Berenzweig, MEd, MA, Child Safety Expert, Mental Health Professional, Educator, Public Speaker, Author, Mom, and Cofounder of KidSafe Foundation

Sally Berenzweig is a former psychotherapist who has a Masters in Elementary Education and a Masters in Counseling Psychology. She has worked with survivors of sexual abuse as well as in private practice. She specializes in child safety, prevention education workshops, and parenting skills. Sally is the coauthor of *KidSafe for Kids,* an 8-week curriculum for children ages 4–11, and two children's books *Jack Teaches His Friends to Be KidSafe!* and the 2011 Literary Award Winning children's book *My Body Is Special and Belongs to ME!*

Cherie Benjoseph, LCSW, Child Safety Expert, Mental Health Professional, Educator, Public Speaker, Author, Mom, and Cofounder of KidSafe Foundation

Cherie has been working in the field of social work since 1989, specializing in children and families. After earning her MSW from Boston University, Cherie took a position as a public school guidance counselor (School Social Worker) in Boston. There she had the opportunity to work with early intervention through middle school students, teachers, and parents. She trained and specialized in violence prevention/conflict resolution, active parenting skills, and her main focus, personal safety. Cherie is the coauthor of *KidSafe for Kids,* an 8-week curriculum for children ages 4–11, and two children's books *Jack Teaches His Friends to Be KidSafe!* and the 2011 Literary Award Winning children's book *My Body Is Special and Belongs to ME!*

For more information about the authors or KidSafe Foundation's programs, please visit www.kidsafefoundation.org

About the Illustrator

Lilah Cohen is an honors student who resides in Florida. Both of her parents are employed in law enforcement and she has three younger siblings and a cat, Red. Her two sisters and brother often serve as inspiration for her drawings. Lilah has been drawing for as long as she can remember and has taken various art courses since she was five. When she is not drawing, Lilah enjoys reading and is an avid fan of art and history.

About the Designer

Gary A. Rosenberg is a graphic designer specializing in books targeted to specific audiences. He met Sally's son, Jack, teaching self defense to local kids, and the collaboration here is an extension of that relationship. He is also co-author (with wife, Carol) of the Jon and Jayne Doe Series of books on socialization for teens and pre-teens (www.jonandjayne.com). Gary works with Carol from their studio in Boca Raton, Florida, serving the editorial and graphic needs of the book publishing industry. For more info, visit www.thebookcouple.com.

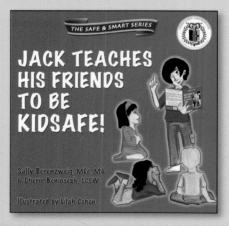